# planet earth
## our extraordinary world

# Ultimate Sticker Book

Modern Publishing
A Division of Unisystems, Inc.
New York, New York 10022
Printed in China
Series UPC: 11733

Printed on
Recycled Paper

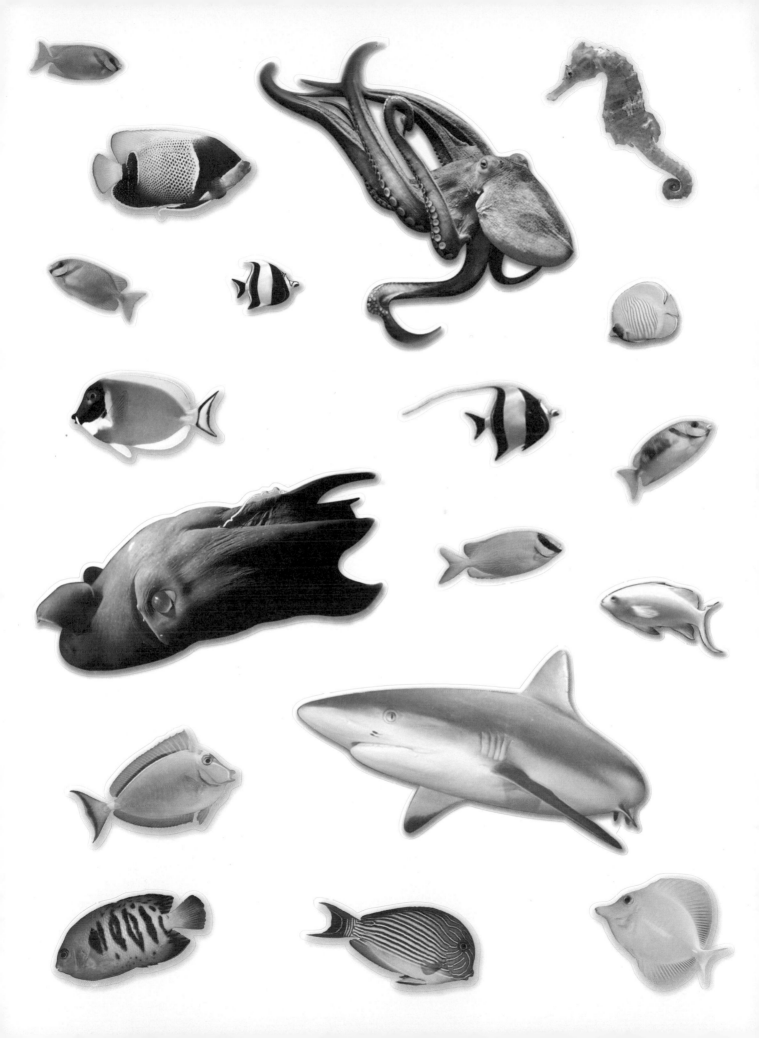

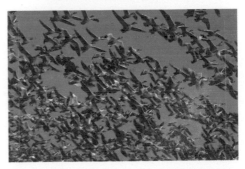

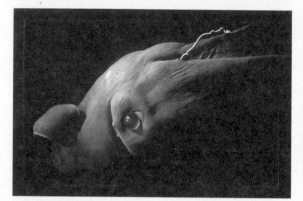

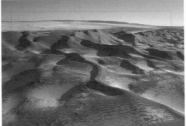

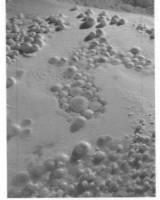